C000076468

everything men understand about women

THE MYSTERIES REVEALED

Dr. A. Ripov & S. K. Harpa

mad
moose
press

Managing Editors: Simon Melhuish and Emma Craven
Series Editors: Simon Melhuish, Emma Craven,
Lee Linford and Nikole G Bamford
Cover Design: Alan Shiner

Designed and compiled by
Mad Moose Press
for
Lagoon Books
PO Box 311, KT2 5QW, UK
PO Box 990676, Boston, MA 02199, USA

ISBN: 1-904139-12-4

www.madmoosepress.com
www.lagoongames.com

Printed in China.

everything
men
understand
about
women

THE MYSTERIES REVEALED

Dr. A. Ripov & S. K. Harpa